This Monster Doodle Book
belongs to ....
....

It's laundry day! What are these monsters hanging on their washing lines?

Claude loves trying on wigs!
Can you draw his new hairdo?

Eek! Who is
hiding under
the bed?

What has Albert
bought from the
Marvellous Monster
Pet Shop?

Who is Ernie playing **tug-of-war** with?

What MEGA munchies are on the menu at the Monster Cafe?

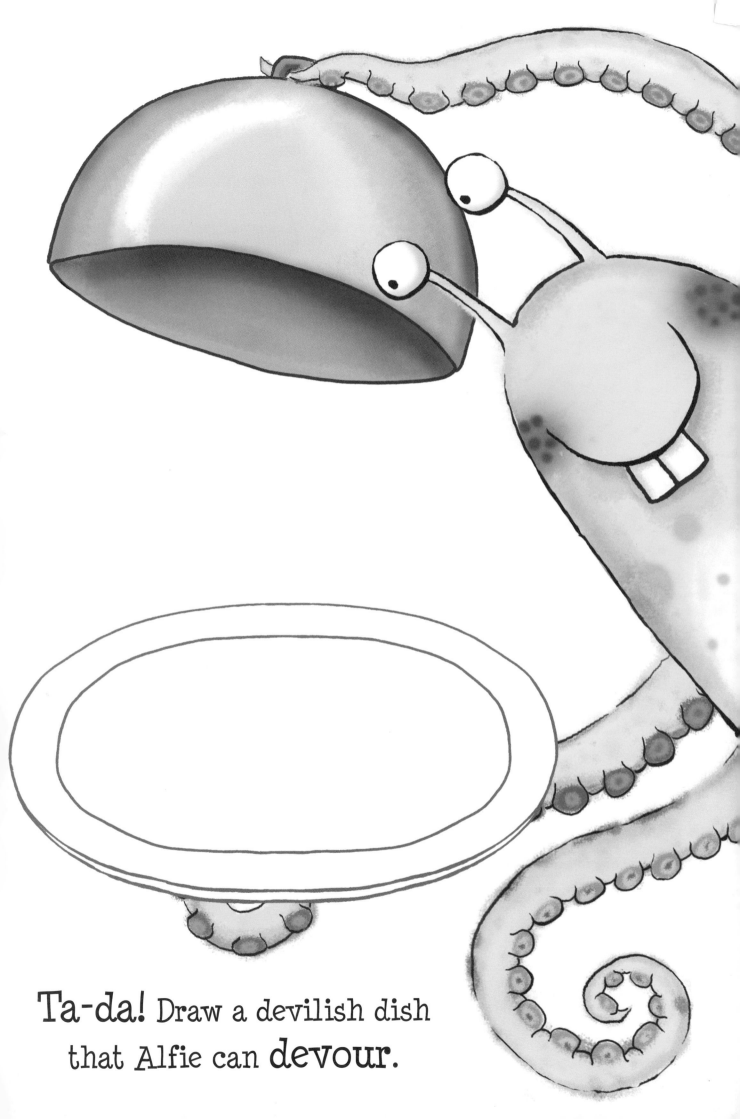

Ta-da! Draw a devilish dish that Alfie can **devour**.

Crack! Who is hatching from this **monster** egg?

crack!

crack!

Ernie is feeling lonely.
Can you give him
something to hug?

Hector just loves **pizza!** Can you draw him some tasty toppings?

What has Gertrude
captured in her claws?

Become a
Monster Maker!
Use these shapes
to create some
crazy creatures.

Mega maths? Slimy science?

What are the little monsters learning at school?

Who's dunking the basketball?

What's the monster munching?

Be careful, Wally!
What's **lurking**
beneath the
tightrope?

What has Rodney caught on his fishing line?

How does the astromonster
blast into space?

Can you doodle
some crater critters?

Arr! Can you draw a monster captain?

Can you draw monsters to match these shadows?

What can Susanna see
outside the window?

Squelch! Who is lurking
in the slimy swamp?

Deborah has spotted something through her telescope. What do you think it is?

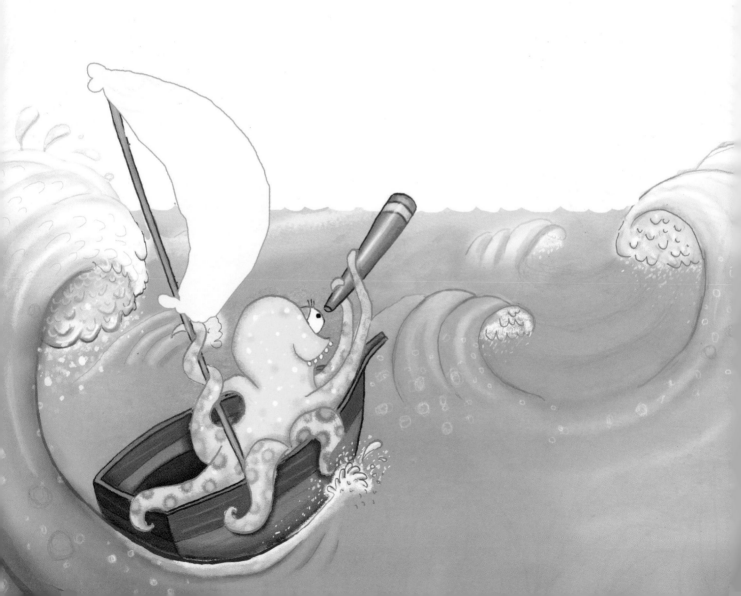

Can you draw some **phantom** photos?

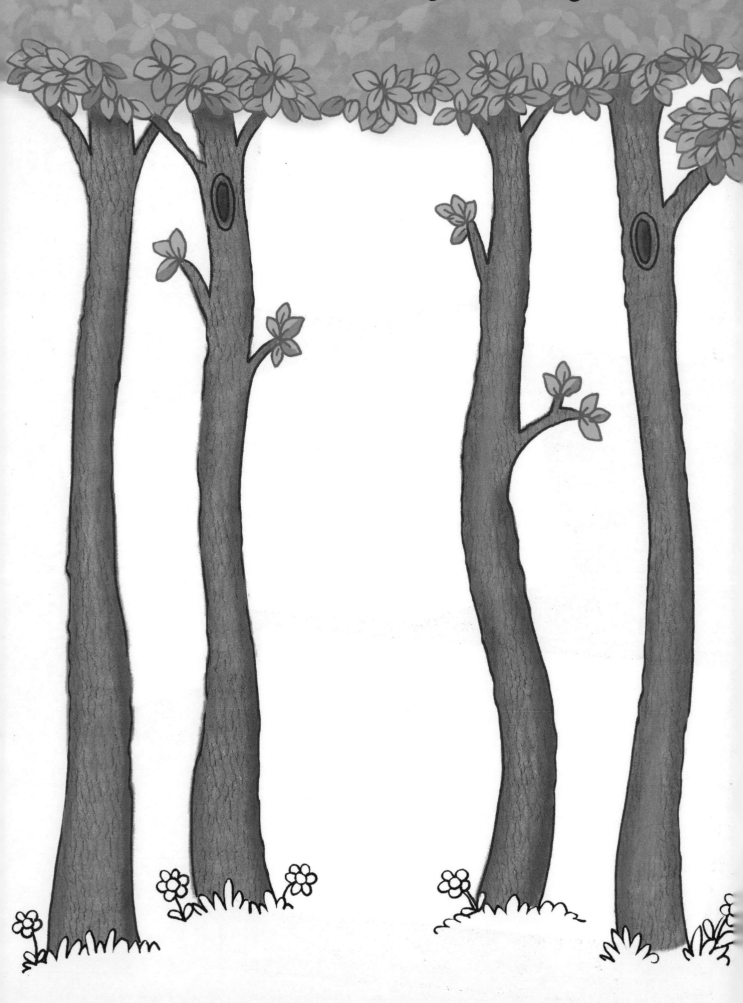

Who's hiding in the **frightening** forest?

Can you draw a cool pattern on Claude's T-shirt?

Bill and Bert need some bodies!

Who is flying the kite?

Whoosh!

Can you finish these monster doodles?

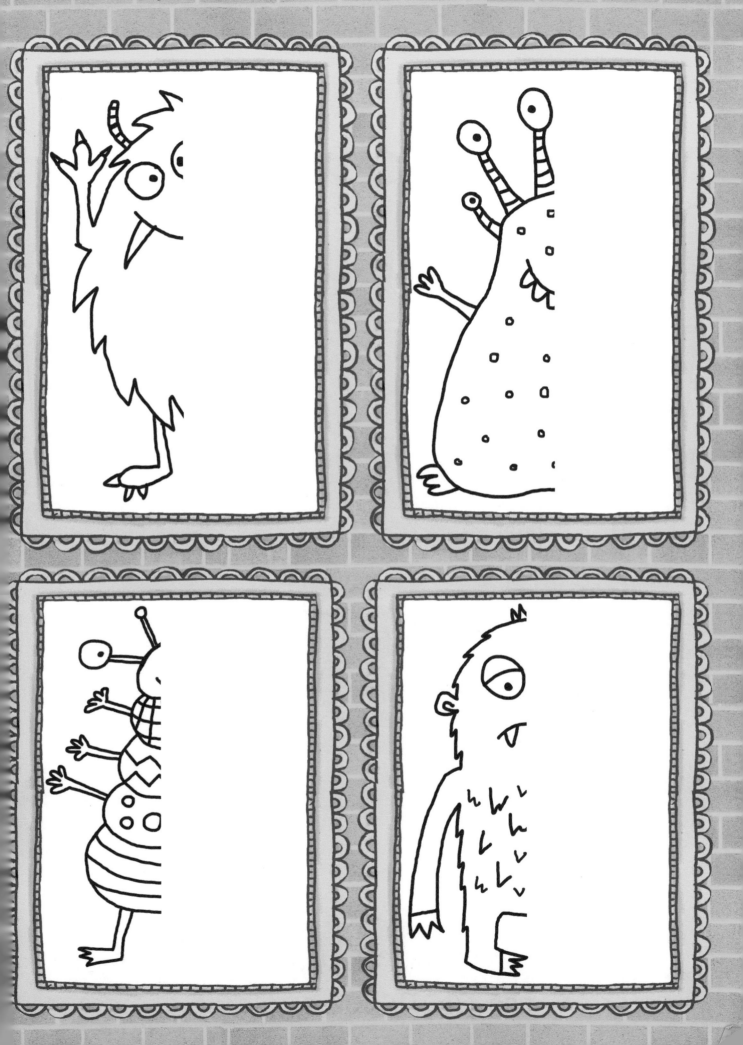

Who's the **king** of
the **monster** castle?

Can you help Nora
paint her monster mural?

Poor Peter is in a *pinch!* What is he stuck in?

Help!

Xerxes likes to X-ray monsters.
Can you sketch their skeletons?

Which monster movie is playing?

What is Alfie standing on?

Can you doodle a house
for this monster?

It's show time!
Who is performing in the spotlight?

Choo! Choo! Who's riding on the monster train?

Buzz!

Buzz!

Buzz!

Buzz!

What is Eric about to **snap** up for lunch?

Can you decorate Yorrick's designer den?

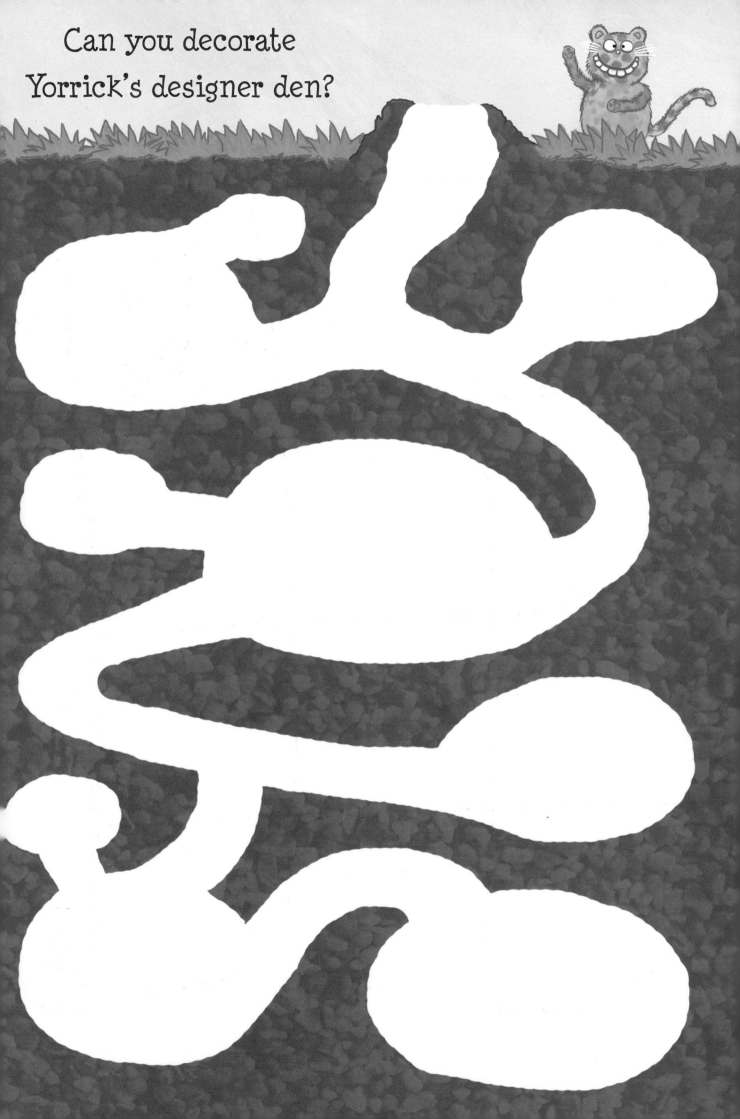

Can you draw a map
to the treasure?

What **beastly bounty** has the monster found?

What are these monsters building?

Can you draw ten tiny monsters hiding in this room?

What slimy sea monsters are hiding in the depths?

Can you draw
Hector's reflection
in the mirror?

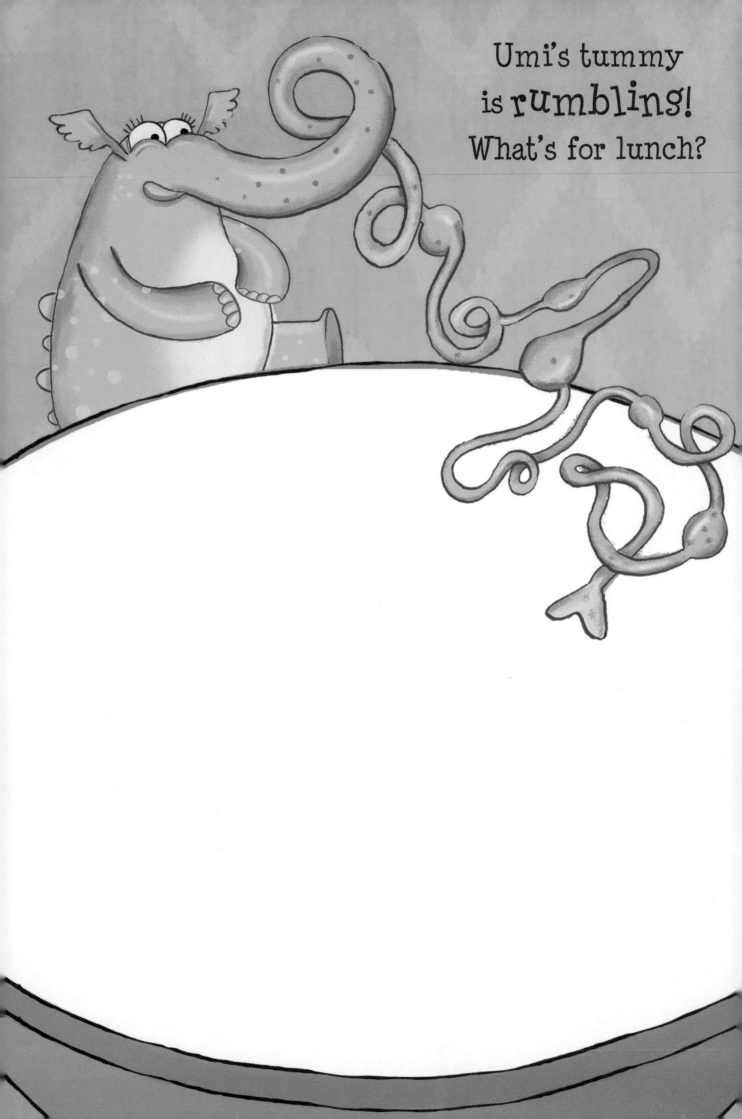

Umi's tummy is **rumbling**! What's for lunch?

What is fearless
Freddie diving into?

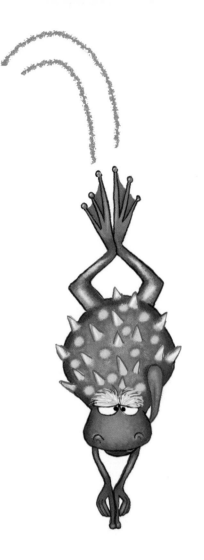

Can you draw these monsters' little terrors?

Mo **loves** hats!
Can you doodle one for her?

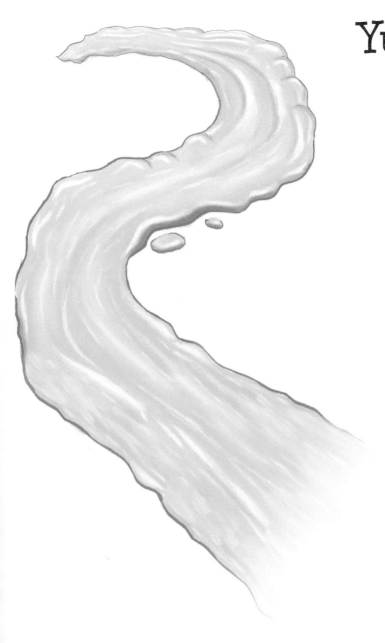

Yuck! Which mucky
monster has left
a trail of slime?

Zzzzz...
What is Zelda
dreaming about?